The internet is amazing. We can stay in touch with our friends, find loads of helpful information, and watch endless funny videos of cats. Sadly, that's not all the internet is. There is a dark side to the internet, where friends aren't nice, information isn't true, and videos aren't cute and hilarious. In our rhymes you will learn about this side of the internet, and get a peek at what lurks Beneath the Screen.

# The picture that will

There were bits of burger stuck in my hair
And cola streaming out of my nose
A funny selfie I thought I'd share
What could go wrong, do you suppose?

The picture was liked over and over again
And I was tagged the Burger Brat
In school I nearly went insane
When people asked: "Do you want fries with that?"

Now my photo's suddenly everywhere
On every computer and every device
I'm living in some sort of waking nightmare
I'm famous – but at what a price!

It seems there's nothing I can do
To put this awful blunder right
I might just as well stick my head down the loo
To convince you that I'm really bright.

Now the picture's been tweeted by someone from Strictly
It's been seen by millions in just one day
It'll still be there when I'm over sixty
The picture that just won't go away.

never go away ......

# The Troll

Grandma's locked herself into the attic
And won't answer me when I call
I hope I don't sound too dramatic
But she doesn't seem to like me at all

I don't understand it, I've done nothing wrong,
We used to be perfectly fine.
On Facebook I said her moustache was quite long,
I never thought she would read that online.

I just wrote some mean stuff about people, that's all
I said they were ugly and fat
So the teachers told Mum and Dad I'm a troll
They had no need to do something like that

Now Dad wears a mask when he drives me to school
And drops me a mile from the gate
He says "That's what you get for being so cruel,
Now start running or else you'll be late"

When I came back from swimming last Saturday night
Mum had changed all the locks on the door
She hid in the wardrobe and turned off the light
And roared "We don't live here no more"

# Jumping Flashback

Emily watched some online horror
And it was a bit too scary for her
She found it hard to leave behind
The monsters roaming around her mind

When she saw her brother splutter and cough
She feared his head might drop right off
And fall to the ground and roll away
So she left the room without delay

And when Dad cut his little finger
Emily thought she'd best not linger
For when the vampires came she'd rather
Not be there when they bit poor Father

When Emily couldn't get to sleep
It didn't help her counting sheep
Zombies would come in enormous numbers
And eat the flock and ruin her slumbers

Now Emily's changed her viewing habits
She watches films about cats and rabbits
The monsters left, with cries and sobs
To look for other haunting jobs

# Puppet Brother

My brother used to drive me crazy,
He'd pinch my arm and pull my hair.
He was silly and loud and funny and lazy
And sometimes I wished he wasn't there.

But it seems like he's just a puppet now,
Someone orders him about and pulls his strings.
So my brother's grounded and this is how
They think they'll protect him from harmful things.

Dad thinks it must be friends at school,
Who were telling my brother what to do.
Like the time he put frogs in the swimming pool,
And stuck the front door shut with glue.

But my brother's best friend is his mobile phone,
And he only talks to people he's met online.
But he's on his computer and safe at home,
So Dad thinks it's all going to be just fine.

My brother never seems to laugh any more,
And though he used to be such a pain,
I wish he'd leave his computer and run out the door,
And be my silly, lazy, funny, loud brother again.

# A girl called

She's your bestest ever Facebook friend
And Oh My God you never
Met anyone you could depend on
Like this girl called Heather

It feels like she can read your mind
As if you've known her like, forever
She's funny, caring nice and kind
Your BFF called Heather

She wants to know just everything
About you and if you ever
Need a friend to help with anything
You could straightaway call Heather

You can say everything to her, it's true
You know you can trust Heather
But one thing Heather never said to you
Is that he's fifty nine and twenty stone and his name is really Trevor

# Heather

True.

They said Andrew's Mum is really fat
They sent me a picture on Snapchat
But I don't agree with that
I said it wasn't true

Shelley's nose is like a hook!
That's what they said on Facebook
I think she's really nice, and look –
I said it wasn't true.
And so did Andrew too.

I'm stupid and smelly and have no friends
That's the message someone sends
But this is where that rubbish ends
I said it wasn't true
And so did Andrew
And Shelley too!

# A Mother's Misery

It was the first week of the holidays when Irshad went away
We keep looking at his picture and we miss him every day

I'd love to meet him one more time and touch his smiling face
But he's not gone to Australia or some exotic place

He's playing online games in his room from morning until night
I don't want to go in there cause I know I'd get a fright

He hasn't showered for days and days and he lives on crisps and sweets
I only know he's still alive from Snapchats and from tweets

His friends don't come to call no more and honestly I doubt
If the house fell down around his ears he'd bother coming out

But soon I'll see my boy again and end this awful sorrow
I haven't paid the broadband bill and he'll be cut off tomorrow

# The Teacher and the tutu

Mr. Chivers explains to his class
The chemical composition of glass
But they don't even pretend to pay attention
They're thinking about something they dare not mention
It's an ancient video they found on YouTube
Of Mr Chivers in a purple tutu

It happened at his college fancy dress
Mr Chivers was out to impress
The girl who later became Mrs Chivers
But now when he thinks of it he shivers
Though in the film he really looks fantastic
And his dancing is certainly most gymnastic

He stops and asks if there's any questions
The class make rather silly suggestions
And ask if he'd show them how to waltz
And whether his boobs were real or false,
The tutu went back to the shop the next day,
But that video is really here to stay.

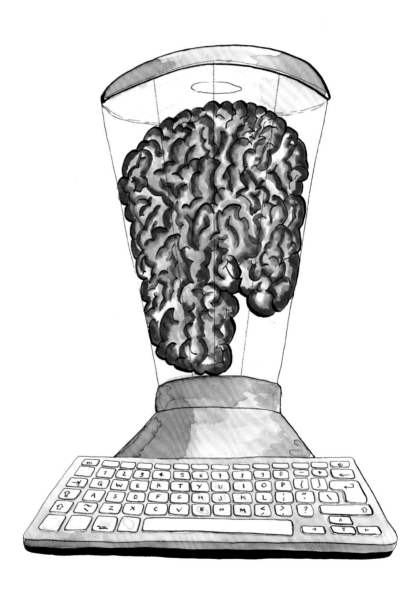

# scrambled Brains

We take your fresh brain, the younger the better
You've spent years in school so it's full up and clever

We put it in front of a screen for the day
Then do that for years in much the same way

We want to make sure you get constant distraction
So every few seconds there's some new attraction

Soon you're not able to pay much attention
To people around you and that's our intention

You'll find that it won't be so easy to think
For your thoughts disappear just as fast as you blink

So please click "accept" to our term and conditions
Forget about school and your lifetime ambitions

No need to ask questions or think very deep
You brain has been scrambled and its now ours to keep

# Hacked off

My profile picture is my photoshopped head,
On a monkey's backside, shiny bright and red.

I changed my status to something I dare not mention
All you need to know is, I got a year's detention

And there's no way now I'll ever go out with Steph
Cos I told the world that she's got bad breath

I've fallen out with my best friend James
By telling everyone I think he has no brains

I confessed to my teacher that I really loved her
And said I want to fight Billy's huge older brother

I gave a thumbs up to things I really don't like
Like Aqeel getting bullied then pushed off his bike

What's really terrible is that no one else can see
All the things I've said I've done, weren't done by me

Someone must have found my password, it was one two three four
I know I gave it out to James but he absolutely swore

He never told a living soul, apart from Ash and Ricky
And no one could have guessed it because it's really tricky

Now I'm scared to check my profile, in case I ever see
Something worse than a monkey's bum pretending to be me.

# You bet I would

I met a stranger in the street today
Who asked for the key of our front door
He said that he'd like me to give away
My name and address and much much more

He wanted to look inside my house
To see my bed and my favourite chair
He promised to be quiet as a little mouse
And my Mum wouldn't know he was even there

He wanted to see lots of photos of me
And pictures of all my friends as well
I thought if I asked them they mightn't agree
But he said it wouldn't be cool to tell

He said I should write all my passwords down
As it would make it easy for us to talk
And asked if we could meet up later in town
To play and go for a little walk

I ran away as fast as I could
I told my teachers and Mum and Dad
I knew that the things he asked me would
Put me in danger and were downright bad.

But if I met that man online today
Would I be as careful as I should?
Would I tell my parents and run away?
I'm very smart and YOU BET I WOULD.